D0201226

YEARNING FOR PEACE

MURAD LAZAR

Copyright © PG 2015, 2020.

All rights reserved. No part of this publication may be reproduced in any form without written permission from the author. yearningfp@gmail.com

ISBN-13: 978-1-61291-645-3

Some of the anecdotal illustrations in this book are true to life and are included with the permission of the persons involved. All other illustrations are composites of real situations, and any resemblance to people living or dead is coincidental.

Unless otherwise identified, all Scripture quotations in this publication are taken from the *Holy Bible, New International Version*® (NIV®). Copyright © 1973, 1978, 1984, 2011 by Biblica, Inc.® Used by permission of Zondervan. All rights reserved worldwide. www.zondervan.com. The "NIV" and "New International Version" are trademarks registered in the United States Patent and Trademark Office by Biblica, Inc.®

Printed in the United States of America

2 3 4 5 6 7 8 9 / 25 24 23 22 21 20

CONTENTS

PREFACE

Yearnings of the Heart

Because Muslims have been such an integral part of my life, I want to be a blessing to you. I have admired and been challenged by your devotion and unashamed loyalty to your religion, your generous hospitality, and your longing for justice. And because of the theological and political arguments for the past fourteen centuries, I felt compelled to reach out at the heart level.

After years of thinking about the subject, I came up with a one-question survey to identify the yearnings of Muslims. I did not want to make guesses at your yearnings. I wanted you to have the dignity of expressing what is of greatest importance to you at the deepest level. It is neither a threatening nor judgmental question. It is simply this: *"If God were to communicate to you in a dream that He would grant you the deepest desires of your heart, what will you ask for?"*

By design it was never meant to be a scientific survey but simply a vehicle to give anecdotal expressions to your deepest longings. As you can guess, answers to this wide-open question varied. The following are some samples of the responses I received:

- "God doesn't need for me to ask Him; He already knows."
- "My daughter will get a good husband."

- "I want to have assurance that my sins will be forgiven."
- "There will not be any more wars in the world."
- "This question is from the devil."
- "I would like my grandmother to come back to life."
- "A good job."
- "I would like to be sure I am going to heaven."

I hope you will be curious enough to explore the possibility of having your deepest desires met through a relationship you may have considered before. It will be a respectful, intellectual, cultural, and spiritual adventure that we can embark on together.

CHAPTER 1

THE DREAM

"You won't believe the dream I had last night!" declared Hakeem to his three backgammon friends. Mustafa, Subhi, and Zuhayr were captivated by the excitement in his voice. They had been coming to this coffee shop almost every Thursday night for fourteen years, enjoying each other's friendship along with the coffee and argeeleh,[1] and sometimes complaining about how the others made avoidable mistakes in their backgammon play. Most of all, these weekly meetings were their opportunity to solve the world's problems, especially the politics of the Arab world.

While the city bus strained and chugged uphill on the one-way street in west Beirut, the four friends were just getting settled in their chairs at the coffee shop on the ground level of the eight-story building across the street from the Lighthouse Pharmacy.

Mustafa was taller than the average Lebanese, lean, a father of three daughters, and probably the most competitive player among them. He opened the mother-of-pearl Syrian-made backgammon set and began putting the black and white pieces in their starting positions.

Zuhayr picked up the tiny pair of dice. Though naturally shy, he wanted to make the first move, secretly hoping for a double

---

[1]   A water filter smoking device, often called hookah.

six. He was short and rotund, never without a black and white keffiyeh,[2] his quiet way of expressing pride in being an Arab.

The waiter appeared with four cups of thick, black Turkish coffee, creating the unforgettable aroma of heated ground coffee beans. Both Zuhayr and Subhi, who were first cousins, signaled to him they were ready to smoke the argeeleh.

Subhi, also on the plump side and with a shiny head, was the life of the party, having an endless supply of local humor. He was quick to respond to Hakeem's enthusiastic statement. "Was your dream anything like the one you had three weeks ago about all the Palestinians in our refugee camps returning to Palestine?"

The fourth partner was Hakeem, often referred to as "Doctore"[3] since that was what his name meant. He was five feet eight inches, with a scar on the left side of his neck, a permanent reminder of the shrapnel that nearly killed him during the Lebanese civil war. Like the others, his age hovered around sixty. This group not only enjoyed Hakeem but also held him in high respect for his professional position as a physician. But his companions had never before witnessed such intensity in their friend as when he mentioned his dream.

"No, no. Nothing like that," replied Hakeem.

"Then what was your unbelievable dream, Doctore?" Zuhayr asked, impatient to start their game.

"In my dream the room became bright and Allah[4] communicated to me in a mental message. He said, 'If I promise to grant you the deepest desire of your heart, what will you ask for?'"There was pin-drop silence as Hakeem spoke. No one rolled the dice, sipped coffee, or smoked the argeeleh.

---

[2] Checkered Arab men's headdress.

[3] Commonly used French pronunciation.

[4] Allah is the historic Arabic word for God used by both Muslims and Christians.

"How do you know it was Allah and not some Jinn?"[5] asked Subhi with a wrinkled forehead.

Hakeem paused thoughtfully. "Obviously, I can't prove it. And Allah forbid, I don't mean that I saw Him. But I had a clear sense that He was speaking to me. Not in a loud voice — just a mental message. I suppose if Allah wants to get a message across, He would give you a strong inner sense that He is the one speaking."

Zuhayr leaned forward, anxious to know what happened next, and whispered, "I've never known you to talk like this, Doctore. You have always been a man of science. While I know you believe in Allah, I never thought of you as a devoted Muslim that gives much attention to matters of faith."

"You are right, Zuhayr," said Hakeem. "I go to the mosque only on special occasions, but this was wonderfully special. I seemed frozen, flat on my back, with a lump in my throat. Tears were flowing down the side of my face. On one hand, I felt so special that Allah would single me out and make such an incredible offer. On the other hand, I cried even more because when I woke up I felt so undeserving and ashamed that I have not taken Him seriously in my life."

Subhi carefully tested his coffee to see if it had cooled enough to sip. "Doctore, pardon me for saying this, but I wouldn't be sharing this with many people if I were you. Some Imams and Sheikhs[6] might deem this as blasphemy: *'You mean to tell me that Allah goes around talking to people?'*

No, no, I would keep this hush hush, Doctore, hush hush for sure."

---

[5] Evil spirit.

[6] Islamic teachers and leaders.

"You all know I am not much of a theologian or a philosopher. I hardly know what is religiously correct," said Hakeem. "All I know is what happened last night was as real as sitting here with you."

Just as Mustafa rolled the dice, from the corner of the room the television news came on. The report was about another Israeli air raid on Gaza in retaliation for some rockets fired into Israeli territory from the Gaza Strip. The conflict between the Israelis and Palestinians seemed to have no end. Each party used the weapons at their disposal to retaliate. Gaza was particularly vexing as one report stated the average person there lived on two U.S. dollars per day.

"Will it ever end?" blurted Mustafa. "Has this not gone on long enough?"

Once the Egyptian soap opera came back on, the friends ordered fresh hot coffee and got back to their game. It wasn't long before Subhi turned his gaze away from the movement of round wooden pieces on the backgammon board and asked Hakeem, "What did you say was Allah's offer to you?"

Hakeem answered, "If I promise to grant you the deepest desire of your heart, what will you ask for?"

"Did you answer Him?" Subhi eagerly responded.

"Not really. When I woke up I was left speechless, riveted to my bed, not knowing what to do next. I was shaking inside with a mix of fear and joy."

"So," Mustafa said, trying to sound casual, "I know this is only a day old, but have you decided what your deepest desire is?"

Hakeem thought about it. "This is an astonishing offer. I don't want to be flippant about it. Who am I to give Allah a shopping list of desires? This morning, while I was making my hospital rounds, I was preoccupied thinking about this instead of my patients. Clearly one of my top desires is peace."

"Doctore," said Subhi, "everyone wants peace. But we have fought each other since the beginning of time. All we hear is promises of peace, but will it ever happen? Take the Arab Spring.[7] It has resulted in very little peace, if any. Actually, in the case of Syria, they have been killing each other for over two years. Maybe they should call it the 'Arab Winter' there. What peace are you going to ask for, Doctore?"

"Subhi, my dear brother, you are right. As a medical professional I have seen many patients over the years. I've noticed a large percentage of their problems are mental. Their bodies are sick because their minds are not at peace. They have inner unresolved conflicts with their relatives, with supervisors, or fellow employees. Conflicts at school or with the irreligious communities—the list seems endless."

Hakeem shook his head sadly and continued, "We all talk about loving each other, but it seldom happens. What do you see on the news? International wars, tribal wars, religious wars, robberies, murders, divorces, sexual exploitation of children. Something is very wrong. We have been meeting here for years trying to solve the world's problems, but nothing changes. Haven't we even had our own share of conflicts?"

Hakeem sighed, "So, what peace am I looking for? No matter what happens outside, I have to begin with a peace inside of me. Why is it that I get very angry so quickly at home? Why did I get angry when I came home three nights ago after an exhausting day and dinner was not on the table? Why did I get so angry with my daughter, Hala, because she was

---

[7] Popular movement toward democracy in the Arab world starting in December 2010.

spending too much time texting her friends and listening to this stupid noise they call music, instead of doing her homework? What is my explosive anger doing to my relationship with my daughter? Does she tell her friends, 'I love my daddy'? Why is it that I can't have a rational, respectful conversation at home like I do at the clinic?"

By now Zuhayr had won the first game and was resetting the pieces for the next one.

"Doctore," interjected Mustafa as he rolled the dice for his second game, "what you have expressed applies to all of us whether we are religious or not. I have a Maronite[8] Catholic friend at work who tells similar stories. We have to search our own hearts first and stop blaming others."

Suddenly tires screeched outside the coffee shop, followed by a crunching sound when a car hit a motorcycle as the rider was pulling out of the sidewalk into the street. All four men shot up from their seats, and within seconds there was a crowd around the scene. Hakeem immediately assumed the physician role and dialed 125 on his mobile phone, reporting the accident and asking for an ambulance. Helped by his friends who were yelling out his credentials, Hakeem was able to push his way through the gathering crowd to reach the fallen man. The injured man was moaning in pain and clutching his bleeding right leg.

As Hakeem gently rolled him over, he felt the red liquid on his right hand and saw it on his shirt sleeve. He quickly stopped the bleeding with a black and white headdress handed to him by a pedestrian. Some people were yelling at the driver of the car for causing the accident. Others were blaming the

---

[8] An Eastern rite Catholic Church in Lebanon.

man on the ground, each arguing for his own perception of the accident. Although quite shaken and undoubtedly in pain, the injured man was not argumentative. He had the presence of mind to thank Hakeem and the pedestrian for their help. In time, the ambulance came with sirens blazing and lights flashing and took the victim, who could not walk on his own. Gradually people dispersed.

As they regrouped, Mustafa, Zuhayr, and Subhi started drawing on their argeelehs again, perhaps to calm their nerves. Hakeem was quick to point out, "See what I mean about the need for peace?"

"How does one live a life of peace?" asked Subhi. "Do you think it's a gift that only some have? Can it be secured through training or self-control? Do we beg Allah for it as if He is reluctant to give it? Do the people who practice yoga really live peaceful lives with their families in this dog-eat-dog business world?"

Zuhayr picked right up: "Is it lack of peace that draws young people to drugs? Is constant tension in families what drives young girls to elope with their boyfriends to get away from the lack of peace in their homes? People struggle with infidelity, divorce, and financial problems every day."

"Wow! We are really serious tonight," said Subhi. "Let me lighten us up with a story I heard from my ninety-year-old father. During these hard economic times, an eighty-year-old man was brought before the judge because he had been stealing from the market. The judge asked him why he had taken a tin of peaches. The old man said that he was hungry. 'How many peaches were in the tin?' 'Six,' said the man. 'Okay, I'll sentence you to six days in jail.' Before the judge could put the gavel down, the old man's wife, who had been quietly standing beside her husband, asked if she could say something. The judge nodded. Very seriously, she said, 'He also took a tin of peas.'"

It took a second to process the subtle humor. Then they all leaned back on their chairs with side splitting laughter.

Noticing the time, Hakeem brought the discussion to an end. "Well, my friends, I'm glad we don't have to go to jail, but this accident and so many of my experiences, including this scar, remind me how unpredictable life is," he said, pointing to the left side of his neck as his voice choked up more than it had before. "I appreciate your listening to my latest unexpected adventure. I am sure this is not the last chapter in the 'book of peace.' Your sincere friendship over the years gives me the freedom to share my deepest feelings with you, and that means a lot. I need to go see how my family is doing. Allah ma'kum."[9]

He got into his late-model Mercedes a block away and drove off.

---

[9] May God be with you.

CHAPTER 2

HEART TO HEART WITH ALLAH

Hakeem changed his plans and drove down to the boulevard along the Mediterranean shore which the Lebonese called the Corniche, where he parked. Walking in the cool of the night, he mulled over Allah's offer. It was calming listening to the waves lapping the shore just a few meters away. A few families were still strolling with their children, even though it was nine o'clock at night. Hakeem walked by a stall on wheels, delighting in the aroma of roasted corn on the cob. The traffic on the four-lane boulevard was still brisk, but he soon moved his attention away from the surroundings.

He reviewed other dreams he had had. None of them had involved the Almighty. How could he be sure this was Allah communicating? Dreams are so elusive, so easily forgotten. Would this one be erased from his memory like others? Could he take that chance, or did he need to answer the question posed to him right away? He repeated the offer to himself, *"If I promise to grant you the deepest desire of your heart, what will you ask for?"* "You know that I am not used to having personal and intimate conversations with You," Hakeem blurted out hesitantly. "I have grown up believing in Your existence. I was taught that You are very powerful. You can do whatever You choose since that is Your divine privilege. I was told that

15

because of Your greatness and Your transcendence from us humans, it is not possible to know You and be personal with You. I also recall hearing I only please You when I obey what You revealed in the Holy Book. But now I feel confused."

Quickening his pace, Hakeem continued. "I'm pretty sure it was You who communicated with me last night. I am very touched and honored by the personal attention You are giving me. I know I don't deserve it as I have not been very serious about religion. Thank You for stimulating me to think about what is really important in life. I don't want to be greedy with Your offer, but is it okay if I express more than one desire?"

If this was truly an opportunity to communicate with Allah, Hakeem decided he'd better come up with more than one "deepest desire." Besides inner peace, what about enough wealth to put his daughter through the best university so that she could have a good life? That would make his parents very proud of him, which of course, was one of his goals in life. It would make him proud, too, giving him bragging rights with his relatives, medical colleagues, and friends. With reasonable wealth, he could secure his fast approaching retirement. He could not only treat his wife to travel and lavish her with gifts, but they could help the poor, as well.

Wait a minute, he thought. *My father did not put me through college. He simply did not have the resources. Are material benefits the truly important things in life? How destructive or fulfilling has wealth been to families? There have been suicides, divorces, extramarital affairs, rebellious children, and drugs. How much turmoil is caused when the wealthy men or women died and all the relatives fought over the inheritance for generations? Can't I help the poor without being wealthy?*

Just as he was contemplating another "deepest desire," his mobile phone rang. It was his wife, Zaina. "Where are you, habeebi?[10] You've never been so late without letting me know. I was very worried about you. What happened? When are you coming home?"

"I'm so sorry, habibti,"[11] Hakeem responded. "You are right. I should have called. I was on my way home from the coffee shop when I felt I needed to take a stroll by the sea. There was an accident in front of the coffee shop, but more importantly, I needed to think about the dream I had last night."

"Dream! What dream? You never said anything to me!"
"I didn't? That's right. I had to leave before seven this morning to do the hospital rounds. I'm sorry, Zaina; I'll be home soon to tell you all about it."

As Hakeem headed to his car to drive home, he kept thinking about wealth. *It is not necessarily a bad thing, he thought, but is that the highest priority of my life? Does that reflect my deepest values?*

An extremely wealthy politician's life had been suddenly snuffed out on this very boulevard several years before. Hakeem was glad he was not involved in national politics. They all talked about peace but never delivered.

As he walked in the door of his home, Zaina blurted out with a tinge of tears, "I'm so relieved to see you, habeebi. Promise me you will not stay away hours on end without letting me know. I was really worried about you. With all the kidnappings and communal killings that have taken place, I couldn't help it. I don't know what I would do without you

---

[10] My beloved (addressing a male).
[11] My beloved (addressing a female).

Hakeem." She took a deep breath. "Now tell me about this dream."

They had been married twenty-seven years. He delighted in her petit frame and olive skin and loved her agitation when she worried about him. Over the years that had not diminished.

"How is our sweet Hala?" asked Hakeem.

"She was so tired today from her school work and long basketball practice that she is already in bed. Now, about the dream . . ."

"I'll need a glass of your delicious rosewater first," he said as he headed for the sofa in the well-furnished villa. "To think that it all happened while I was sleeping next to you, and you had no idea what was going on."

"What happened?" shouted Zaina as she raised both hands with palms up. "Tell me."

"At some point in my dream the room brightened up, and I received a gentle, but firm message in my mind, 'If I promise to grant you the deepest desire of your heart, what will you ask for?'"

"What language was it in?" "Arabic. Our mother tongue."

Moving closer to him, Zaina asked, "Was it your uncle Abdullah who died last year?"

"No," laughed Hakeem.

"Did you actually hear an audible voice?"

"Not really. It was more like I was being given a message in my mind."

"From a female?"

Smiling, Hakeem answered, "I don't think so." "Then who was it?"

"I think it was Allah!" "Is that possible?"

"Yes, indeed."

After a second of puzzling, Zaina came back with, "How can you be so sure?"

"Habibti, you know I have not been a religious man. I barely have time to scratch my head most days. The few times I have seriously thought about life's purpose, my role in it, and whether I've truly discovered the truth behind it all, it was overwhelming. Honestly, Zaina, I've even asked myself what I really believe. I am not sure. I never invested any time exploring real answers because it seemed beyond me. But this dream is compelling me to think about these things much more seriously."

"The sheikh is not going to be happy if he hears this," moaned Zaina.

"I feel . . . I feel . . ." Hakeem felt a lump in his throat and could not get the words out. Tears began to trickle down his cheeks. Zaina drew closer to him and put her arm around his shoulder, squeezing him tightly. "Habeebi, this dream has really affected you, hasn't it?"

Wiping his cheeks, he said, "Indeed it has. I haven't been able to think of anything else when I am not occupied with work or other responsibilities. On one hand, I feel so honored that He would select me to make such an amazing offer. On the other hand, I feel so ashamed that I have not taken my relationship with Him seriously and have focused on science all these years."

"But as a scientist," said Zaina, "don't you need more proof that it was really Allah communicating with you in this way?"

"Valid question, habibti. I'm afraid I don't have a scientific proof. All I can tell you is the experience I had was real, and the confidence I have in my gut about it is beyond science.

I can't recall another event in my entire life that has driven me to such soul searching."

Zaina could clearly tell this was not the casual evening conversation she usually had with Hakeem.

"Oh, I'm so sorry," she said. "I was so taken up with your dream that I completely forgot you have not had dinner. Hala and I had mujadara[12] and hummus. Would you like that, or do you want me to fix you something else?"

"That will be just fine."

---

[12] Dish of rice, lentils, onions, olive oil, and seasonings.

CHAPTER 3

AN UNUSUAL PATIENT

As Hakeem drove to the American University Hospital the next day, he again mulled over how he would respond to Allah's offer.

He had lived all his life in the turbulence of Middle East politics and wars, and had seen the atrocities of the Lebanese civil war between 1975 and 1990. He had grown up hearing of his parents' exodus from Palestine during the 1948 Arab-Israeli war. Hakeem thought of peace as his number-one wish. As a physician, he was sensitive to human suffering, and when countless deaths and even more injuries were involved, it pained him deep inside.

He was aware of the plight of refugees, the squalor of their camps that had hardly changed in two generations. Then there were the religious, political, ethnic, and economic challenges of so many groups in the Middle East. These included rivalries between Sunni and Shia Muslims, the Alawites of Syria, the Druze of Lebanon and Syria, the Maronites and Orthodox, Hezbullah, the Palestine Liberation Organization, and Hamas. How does one find peace under such circumstances?

Every war had left vast numbers of refugees, unemployed fathers, maimed children, broken families, malnutrition, emotional scars, and little hope for higher education.

As his car inched its way through the bumper-to-bumper traffic on the narrow streets of west Beirut, Hakeem's heart was heavy. *I can always blame local politicians and those with stronger powers or ambitious clergy for atrocities, corruption, or injustice. But where has that gotten us? The cycles are repeated over and over, year after year, century after century. No matter which political figures we vote for or prefer, there seem to be no permanent solutions. It's easy to become disillusioned, cynical, and hopeless.*

Peace was definitely high on Hakeem's list. But it seemed to him that something deeper might be at the root of all this. He had seen patients conflicted in themselves as they struggled with bitterness, anger, hatred, and vengeance. He had experienced intergenerational feuds between his family and his cousin's family. He had seen the internal politics within the medical field, where some people were promoted on the basis of whom they knew and not how they had performed.

Finally arriving at the hospital, Hakeem parked in the physicians' reserved parking and made his way to his office. On the way he passed by the cafeteria, where he got his daily cup of Turkish coffee before starting his rounds. Today the coffee seemed particularly tasty. After printing out the list of patients he was to visit, he donned his white physician's coat and slipped his stethoscope around his neck.

In Room 426 there was a new patient. After being treated in the emergency room the night before for injuries from a motorcycle accident, Mahmoud Ramadan wore bandages over his wounds.

Hakeem recognized Mahmoud immediately and introduced himself: "Sabah al khair.[13] I'm Dr. Husseini. I'm sorry about your experience last night. You may not remember me, but I happened to be in a coffee shop across the street from

---

[13] Good morning.

your accident and was able to stop your bleeding before the ambulance came."

"Allah bless your children, Doctore. Thank you very much for what you did for me," hurried Mahmoud.

The doctor continued, "Your X-rays show no broken bones, but you are going to be sore for a while. We will do everything to get you back on your feet. On a scale of one to ten, how would you describe your level of pain right now?"

"About seven. It's an honor to meet you, Doctore Husseini," said Mahmoud. "Thank you very much again for helping me at a critical time yesterday. How interesting that your first name matches your profession. After the slow-dragging night hours in emergency, it is a relief just to see you. The pain in my right leg is very uncomfortable, but, thanks to my Lord, I am experiencing peace about the whole situation.

"Frankly, Doctore, my immediate concern is for my fellow patient, Mr. Zahreddine. He was injured in some communal fighting the Druze community endured yesterday. He had a very difficult night, and I will feel much better if you attend to him first."

Lifting his brow, Hakeem said, "In my thirty-three years of medical practice, I've never had a patient make that request, Mr. Ramadan. You could have lost a leg last night, yet you are at peace and are more concerned for the patient in the next bed, who is also from a different religion than about yourself. Ya salam![14] OK, I'll see him, then come back to you."

Returning to Mahmoud Ramadan several minutes later, the doctor made sure the right steps were being taken to treat this patient. He discarded his plastic gloves as he exited the room.

---

[14] Wow!

Hakeem seldom had lunch, but today he dropped by the cafeteria again, picked up a chicken sandwich, and returned to his office to mull over a phrase the unusual patient in Room 426 had used: "Thanks to my Lord, I am experiencing peace about the whole situation." What a strange thing to say! Hakeem pondered why Mahmoud, clearly a Muslim, had used the uncharacteristic term "my Lord." Why not *Allah*? There was something very personal about how he referred to Him. It was almost as though he knew Him, something beyond merely having a belief system. Was this some kind of a sign Allah was giving Hakeem about his yearning for peace? He was determined to find out more.

Before leaving the hospital, he stopped by once again to check on his new patient. "Marhaba.[15] How are you feeling now, Mr. Ramadan?"

The patient responded with a winsome smile. "Somewhat better, but please call me Mahmoud, Doctore," he said. "They performed some tests and seemed optimistic I may be able to go home tomorrow. That's good news."

"I have not seen the results yet, but rest assured I'll discharge you as soon as we confirm you will be fine on your own," said Hakeem.

"Thank you, Doctore, I owe you a debt of gratitude," Mahmoud responded with a profoundly sincere look on his face. "Although my injury was the result of an accident," he explained, "your presence nearby was not. I'm so grateful my Lord arranged for you to be there to stop the bleeding as quickly as you did."

Hakeem could no longer hold back his curiosity. "Candidly,

---

[15] Greetings.

Mahmoud, you piqued my interest this morning, and now again, when you referred to Allah as 'my Lord'. This expression is not commonly used among us Muslims. You seem to have some sort of a personal connection with Him. I am just beginning a spiritual journey myself, so I would like to know more about yours. Permit me to ask you something personal. Are you a Sufi?"[16]

"Doctore Husseini," responded Mahmoud, "it will take some time to relate my story. I know you are a busy man. Perhaps we can meet together after I have fully recovered. Suffice it to say it all started about two years ago with a dream. I'd never had one like it before, nor have I had one like it since. May I call you and make an appointment to have coffee together?"

Though he managed to maintain a controlled, professional exterior, Hakeem was beside himself with joy, his inner being quaking with excitement. Could this man's dream have been anything like his own? Though the difference in their social classes gave him some hesitation, he impulsively took out a business card, wrote his mobile number on it, and handed it to Mahmoud. "By all means, call me. I look forward to talking with you." There was something about the joyful, peaceful, and selfless demeanor of this patient that made Hakeem trust him.

---

[16] A more mystical version of Islam.

CHAPTER 4

THE CALL

When Hakeem arrived at the coffee shop, his friends had already set up the backgammon board, and play was underway between Mustafa and Subhi. The men stopped playing and greeted their friend with warm embraces and the traditional three kisses alternating on each cheek. They welcomed him with the customary questions asked in rapid-fire fashion with no pause for answers to be given.

"How are you? Insha Allah,[17] you are happy. How is your health? How is your family? How is the work at the hospital?" asked Subhi.

"Any other dreams, Doctore?" Zuhayr teased.

"No," said Hakeem, "but I have been thinking about the question ever since I left you."

He checked his watch and added, "Make sure I don't stay too late tonight. My wife was upset last time. Wives are always upset when we are late. Why is time important? Enjoying each other is more important than living by the clock. I think that is a leftover from French and British colonialism." Hakeem was thinking out loud, but his friends nodded in agreement.

"While that is true, you have to consider how our wives feel. They have every reason to worry about us considering all the kidnappings and killings that are taking place," Mustafa said.

---

[17] God willing.

"I guess you are right," Hakeem agreed.

Zuhayr jumped in: "Americans seem to be the worst at being slaves to the clock. I have just started a business deal with an American company, and let me tell you, you have to be right on time, every time."

Changing the subject, Subhi asked Hakeem, "So what have you decided to ask Allah for?"

"Peace," replied Hakeem.

"That makes sense," Mustafa said. "Everywhere you turn, there is trouble and conflict. My cousin's family has been fighting with us for three generations. How stupid is that? The Syrians are always trying to control things. The Americans are always meddling in our affairs. You know they are involved because of the oil."

Subhi surprised them with, "Turning to a more personal level, there's plenty of turmoil in my conscience."

"Why your conscience?" asked Mustafa.

"Money is the big culprit in messing up relationships between families," Subhi explained. "I borrowed some money from an uncle and have not paid him back yet. As a result, things are definitely messed up between us. My conscience tells me I am neither pleasing Allah nor my uncle. I am not at peace."

The words continued to tumble out of Subhi's mouth. "At work there is so much jealousy and favoritism. Without wasta[18] you can never get ahead. I have been a leading marketing rep for fifteen years, and they just made a thirty-year-old woman my manager—just because she is a niece of the owner. I feel like screaming.

---

[18] People of influence who get things done for you—"who you know."

"There is real turmoil in my brother Abdullah's family. He had invested a lot of money with Lehman Brothers, and when they declared bankruptcy, he lost it all. It included money for his five children's university education, his retirement, and caring for his wife's parents in their old age. It's all gone. He is devastated, and unable to sleep at night. No peace there."

Subhi's tirade was interrupted by the ringing of Hakeem's mobile phone.

When he answered, a jovial voice said, "Marhaba, Doctore. Keefak?[19] I hope you are well."

"Who is speaking?" the doctor inquired, not recognizing the voice.

"Mahmoud Ramadan, your very grateful patient from the motorcycle accident."

"Oh, yes, of course, Mr. Ramadan. How are you feeling?" asked Hakeem.

"Much better, thank the Lord." There was that term again. "How is your family? When can we have coffee together?"

"Actually, Mr. Ramadan, when I related our conversation to my wife Zaina, she insisted I invite you and your wife to our home for dinner. How about a week from this coming Sunday at seven o'clock? We live at 45 Rue Clémenceau in west Beirut. If you have trouble finding it, just call me."

"That is very kind of you, Doctore. I feel highly honored. My wife and I will look forward to enjoying your company. Ma issalami."[20]

---

[19] How are you?
[20] Go with peace.

"Which lucky patient gets to have dinner at your home?" asked Subhi.

"Well, it's an interesting story," said Hakeem. "Somehow I think it is related to the question I was asked in my dream."

"Seriously?" Subhi inquired.

"You may not believe this, but the patient who just called is none other than the man who had the motorcycle accident across the street from here. His name is Mahmoud Ramadan. I walked into his hospital room knowing he had been in a potentially serious condition the night before. When I expressed my sympathy for his misfortune, he said that he was at peace with his situation and asked me to first pay attention to his fellow patient who was suffering more than he."

"His roommate must have been a close personal friend," Subhi concluded.

"No, he wasn't," said Hakeem.

Hakeem's friends leaned forward eagerly, with eyebrows and curiosity raised. Hakeem went on, "I've never seen a patient behave this way. We all know how people act when waiting in line. Whether in the bakery, grocery, or even in traffic, they want to step in front of you all the time. Here is a man who was injured and in pain, yet he was more concerned about his fellow patient than himself, and he summarized his entire situation by saying he was thankful to his 'Lord.' Do you know any Muslims who use the term 'my Lord'?"

Mustafa responded, "None of the ones I know. I suppose there could be some. Is it respectful to talk about the Almighty in such familiar terms? Come to think of it, I think I recall one reference like that in the Quran."

"I have to admit," said Hakeem, "there was such serenity about Mahmoud. He was truly at peace. It seemed that his concern for his fellow patient was sincere and was connected to the way he related to Allah. Since I am asking Him for peace, I want to know more."

Zuhayr drew deeply on the argeeleh. Subhi and Mustafa went back to throwing the dice and moving their black and white pieces on the board. Just then, Zuhayr's phone sounded the tune of the Lebanese national anthem.

"Aloo?"

As he listened, he became more agitated and rose to his feet, dropping the mouthpiece of the argeeleh. "When did this happen?" After a pause, he said, "I'll be right over."

"What's going on, Zuhayr?" asked the doctor.

"They kidnapped him . . . my brother," Zuhayr said, clearly in shock and struggling to find words. "It seems my younger brother has been kidnapped."

"By whom?"

"I don't know."

"This is terrible! I am so sorry," Hakeem said in a state of panic. "What can we do to help? Is there someone important we can call to get him released?"

"I need to go. Keep in touch by phone." Zuhayr half tripped over the leg of the table in his rush to get out of the coffee shop.

"I'm coming with you," shouted Subhi, running after him.

With Hakeem and Mustafa left to themselves, they stared at each other, consternation evident on their faces. Finally Mustafa blurted out,

"Will this ever end? What in the world is happening? It's either shootings or kidnappings, bombs or family fights, government corruption or bribery. Just think of the dozens of people in Zuhayr's family who are worried right now. I'm sure they are afraid, yelling, blaming, or conniving to seek revenge on the kidnappers. The women are weeping uncontrollably. Allah ynajjcena.[21] Oh, how we long for peace."

The television program playing at the coffee shop was interrupted by breaking news. Israel could be expected to raid Lebanon again because rockets had been fired into northern Israel from southern Lebanon.

"We better go home, Mustafa," Hakeem warned. "Our families are probably worried."

---

[21] May God rescue us.

CHAPTER 5

ON THE PATH TO PEACE

On the appointed Sunday evening, Mahmoud rang the door-bell. Zaina opened the door, in chic western clothing, with Hakeem standing slightly behind her. They both welcomed their guests with "Ahlan wa sahlan."[22] After making introductions, Zaina received the gifts brought by Mahmoud and his wife, Hayat—a bouquet of flowers and a box of chocolates. "You didn't need to do this," Zaina said politely.

"It's a very small way of expressing how honored we feel to be invited to your home," responded Mahmoud. Zaina noticed that Hayat was in more conservative attire.

The visitors were ushered in and seated in the living room, feeling a bit ill at ease as they had clearly come into a higher social-class home than they were used to. They couldn't help noticing the modern furniture and art work on the walls that indicated foreign travel.

As tea was set before the guests by a young maid, Hayat asked, "How are your children?"

Zaina quickly answered, "We have just one daughter, Hala. She is with her uncle's family in the mountains for the long weekend."

---

[22] You are welcome.

Hakeem took over the conversation with sincere delight. "I'm very glad you are here and that no sectarian fighting kept you from coming. Have you healed well from your wounds?"

"Thanks to your help, I'm healing well," said Mahmoud. "You probably noticed I'm walking with a slight limp, but it is much improved, thanks to my Lord."

"I'm glad to hear that. Injuries like yours take time to heal. Feel free to come back to the hospital if you need more help. How are your children?"

"Thank the Lord, they are fine," answered Mahmoud.

There we go again. What's with this man's seeming intimacy with the Almighty? thought Hakeem.

"Forgive me for being so forward," he said, "but we doctors learn to get to the point quickly since we have so many patients to attend to." Before he could get any further, however, Zaina stepped forward to announce dinner was ready. "Tfudduloo."[23]

Once the plates were full of aromatic Lebanese food, the doctor wasted no time bringing up the topic of his dream. "I need to tell you about a dream I had not long ago. In my dream, the room became bright, and I received this mental message, 'If I promise to grant you the deepest desire of your heart, what will you ask for?'

"Now, I'm not a very religious man, but I was brought up to believe in Allah and the Prophet (pbuh). There was no question in my mind the One communicating with me that night was Allah. If you ask me how I know with such certainty, all I can say is, I just know. As I have thought about what I would ask Him for, one of the deepest desires of my

---

[23] Please come to the table.

heart is to experience peace in my inmost being."

He took a bite, and when the others remained silent, he continued.

"I don't have to tell you our world is a mess. People, the economy, politics, social services—whole cultures are affected by the designs of selfish, cruel, corrupt, and hypocritical forces. Even my honorable medical field is filled with political positioning for power, greed, and unfair treatment of patients."

Zaina passed around a plate of rice while Hakeem continued. "As you can see, Mahmoud, we are living comfortably, thanks to Allah. We have enough income to afford the pleasant things of life—house, furnishings, works of art, travel abroad, good education for my daughter and my brother's children, and an honorable name. But as I have examined my own life, I know I am not at peace inside. I don't experience your kind of peace." The doctor stopped for a breath. His guests appeared undisturbed by his transparency. He looked down at his plate and continued. "Forgive me for talking so much. When I encountered you in the hospital, I saw a seriously injured man who did not deserve to be injured, demonstrating an appealing level of peace. You could have been very bitter about what happened to you, wanting revenge on the driver of the car that hit you. Instead, you were more concerned about your fellow patient.

"The other thing that struck me was the very natural way in which you used the term 'my Lord,' as though He is very real to you, as though you have something like an intimate relationship with Him. I was taught He is powerful, merciful, gracious, a judge to be revered, whose final decision regarding our eternal destiny we will not know until the last day."

Zaina had been listening intently to her husband baring his soul. "Hakeem, I have never heard you talk like this. Is this why you have been so quiet lately? I thought it was because of stress from work."

Hakeem acknowledged his wife, then turned to Mahmoud, looking deeply into his eyes. "Mahmoud, help me understand how Allah seems to be so real to you."

Mahmoud swallowed his last piece of pita bread and adjusted himself in his seat. "First of all, let me thank you from the bottom of my heart for welcoming us into your home and letting us eat at your table. It is such an honor. The only place I have met a doctor before is in a hospital.

"I also honor you for the honest way in which you speak. As your gracious wife Zaina says, you have bared your heart. I respect that level of humility. It seems this dream has caused you to do some soul-searching like I did. You are not hiding behind religious tradition or intellectual sophistication.

"Strangely enough, my story also involves a dream. You know how we Arabs pay attention to our dreams."

Zaina swallowed hard, wondering what was going on with all these dreams, and if she would ever experience one.

"I was thirty-six years old, very faithful in my duties as a Muslim, but I had a deep desire to enjoy Allah, not just work hard to please Him. Then I had this dream in which I was directed to read the Injil.[24] I decided to contact my Armenian classmate of nineteen years earlier to get a hold of an Injil. Garo Mazmanian had an Arabic version mailed to me since he was teaching overseas. I started reading from page one.

---

[24] New Testament part of the Bible.

"The life of Isa, known as Yasou[25] in the Arabic Injil, was fascinating. But there was one story in the third book, written by a man named Luke, I found particularly moving. By the way, just for your interest, I later found out Luke was a physician. The story is about a father who had two sons who were not enjoying living and working with him."

Intrigued, Zaina asked, "So what did Luke say about why these two sons were not enjoying their father?"

Mahmoud replied, "It seems these boys were adults, and the younger one announced to his father one day that he wanted to live his own life independently. He asked his father for his share of the inheritance."

"What a disrespectful boy!" shouted Hakeem. "His father should have slapped him hard for dishonoring him like that. Everyone knows the only time an inheritance is divided among the children is when the father dies. The son was telling his own father, 'I wish you were dead.' Sorry for interrupting you, Mahmoud, but I'm sure the father was furious at him. And why didn't the older brother scold him?"

"As I read the story several times, I too was upset at the boy," replied Mahmoud. "Dr. Luke does not tell us if the older son was present when this conversation took place. Even if he was, maybe he was glad to get rid of his younger brother since they were not getting along. Doesn't it sound like some dysfunctional families today? What shocked me was the father's response. He did the unthinkable and gave the boy his share of the estate and let him go."

"How could he do that?" blurted Zaina.

---

[25] For the Quranic reference to Jesus I have used "Isa." For the Arabic word for Jesus in the New Testament of the Bible, I have used "Yasou" instead of "Yasou3" which indicates one of the guttural sounds in Arabic.

Hayat finally chimed in, "Maybe he thought the only way the boy would learn his lesson was to be on his own and find out what life was really like on the outside."

Mahmoud continued, "The boy travelled to another country, wasted his money on human passions, and when he ran out of money, he also lost his fair-weather friends. To make things worse, just when he had run out of money, a famine hit the region. He was one hungry lad."

"He must have broken his mother's heart, too," said Zaina. "How is it we don't hear about her?"

"It would have killed me if that were my son," agreed Hayat. "Maybe she had died before this happened."

"The only way the boy survived was to hire himself out to a farmer who raised pigs," Mahmoud said. "I could imagine how shameful and degrading that must have been to a man from his culture. Then Luke says, 'When he came to his senses, he said, "How many of my father's hired servants have food to spare, and here I am starving to death! I will set out and go back to my father and say to him: Father, I have sinned against heaven and against you. I am no longer worthy to be called your son; make me like one of your hired servants." '

Hakeem chimed in, "Looks as if he is finally learning how good his father had been to him."

"Indeed," responded Mahmoud. "What happens next really touched my heart. It seems that the boy's father was fairly wealthy, having land, cattle, and servants. That would mean the people of his village would have known him and would have been very angry that he was treated so disrespectfully by his younger son. They may have even lost respect for this man for letting his son go.

"Evidently this father longed for his son to return. Every

day he would look into the distance to see if he was coming back," said Mahmoud, cupping his hand in front of his forehead. "Sure enough, one day the father recognized the boy at a distance, slowly making his way back to the village.

"As I tried to put myself in the father's shoes, I think I would have stayed at the house with my formal robe on and my arms folded, waiting for the boy's apology. I would be eager to exercise my authority in deciding his punishment since justice was what he deserved. But what his father did moved me so deeply that I began to cry. Hayat will tell you I seldom cry." Hayat moved her head up and down, her lips parting in a slight smile.

"What did he do?" asked Zaina, leaning forward.

"He ran from his house down the road through the village to meet his son. In order to run, he would have to pick up the hem of his kumbaz,[26] thus showing his knees. You can imagine the children in the streets running behind him and taunting him. Here was a respected and honorable leader in the village, allowing himself to be mocked by people who probably gossiped behind his back. The father's behavior toward the returning son was unheard of in that culture."

Hakeem observed, "It looks as if the father set aside his dignity to love his son. I wonder how much he had been suffering in his heart for his son's sake. I'm sure it was painful to have people either ignore him when they passed by or give him a brief greeting under their breath."

Mahmoud nodded while Hakeem pressed for more of the story. "Then what happened?" he asked, raising his right hand and pitching his voice higher.

---

[26] Long robe.

"Dr. Luke goes on to say, 'But while he was still a long way off, his father saw him and was filled with compassion for him; he ran to his son, threw his arms around him and kissed him. "The son said to him, 'Father, I have sinned against heaven and against you. I am no longer worthy to be called your son.' "But the father said to his servants, 'Quick! Bring the best robe and put it on him. Put a ring on his finger and sandals on his feet. Bring the fattened calf and kill it. Let's have a feast and celebrate. For this son of mine was dead and is alive again; he was lost and is found.' So they began to celebrate" (Luke 15:20-24).

"It's hard to comprehend what a heart of love this father had for his wayward son," marveled Hakeem. "It seems he was more concerned about their relationship than bringing about justice for the shame and indignity he had suffered. The village people were probably expecting some type of punishment, but instead, the father was compassionate."

"Doctore, you are absolutely right," Mahmoud said. "And that's the conclusion I came to, as well. There is more to the story, but I don't want to take up your whole evening. What touched me was the character of the father, who was willing to suffer in order to demonstrate the extent of his love for his son, even though the son did not deserve it."

Hayat interjected, "Mahmoud, tell them what you discovered about who was actually telling the story that Dr. Luke wrote down."

"The story was told by Isa. He was talking with religious leaders who were complaining about His associations with sinful people. He used three stories to give a picture of what Allah is like—that He is full of love and compassion, even suffering the effects of people's rebellion, yet ready to receive them back into His family and to celebrate when they repent. The story about the two sons is the third one."

"What were the other two?" asked Zaina with characteristic curiosity.

Mahmoud replied, "They are both very interesting, but I see it's getting late, and I'm sure your husband has to be up early to make his hospital rounds. Perhaps we could meet again and discuss the other two.[27] We would be very honored if you would come to our humble home."

"Mahmoud," interjected Hakeem, "I appreciate your thoughtfulness, but before you leave, I'd like to know one thing. What is the relationship between this story and your experiencing peace and enjoying personal intimacy with the Almighty?"

"Doctore Husseini," responded Mahmoud, "the story of the father and two sons was just the starting point of a journey I made to satisfy my curiosity about Isa. If He had such insight into the character of Allah, whom He called Father, I wanted to know what else He did and taught. Consequently, I read and reread all four accounts of His life in the Injil, as well as the rest of the books in the Injil. I found information that I simply had not heard before. I came across details that no one had taught me, and, frankly, I fell in love with Him. I know that is a strange way for an Arab man to express himself, but I had a curious mind and seeking heart, and to me, Isa was irresistible."

Hakeem could not help but ask, "Does this mean you are Christian now?"

"It's not quite as simple as that," answered Mahmoud.

---

[27] The three stories Jesus told are found in Luke 15:1-32.

"Since it is getting late, shall we continue this conversation at another time?"

"No, no," insisted Hakeem, unconcerned about the time. "It's okay. What I want to know is how you experienced such peace and intimacy with Allah."

"Let's say I have come to a new understanding of the Isa that Luke writes about," Mahmoud answered. "Even though I was a serious Muslim, one of the realities of my life before coming to love Isa was that no matter how devout I was, there was this restlessness in my inner being. I was not at peace with myself, with Allah, and often with people. I was restless about the guilt and shame I experienced when I felt I was not measuring up to Allah's expectations. I had no way of knowing if my good deeds exceeded my bad deeds, and I could only hope that Allah would be merciful on judgment day and allow me into heaven. Still, I had no assurance of this."

"Doesn't everyone have that anxiety?" asked Zaina.

"I believe most people do to one extent or another. But I wanted answers," said Mahmoud. "The more I read about the life of Isa, the more I found that He is the source of peace. He promised, 'Peace I leave with you; my peace I give you. I do not give to you as the world gives. Do not let your hearts be troubled and do not be afraid.'"

Hakeem couldn't wait any longer and blurted out, "I find that enticing but what is unique about Isa's peace?"

"Remember the father reaching out to the returning son by sacrificing his dignity and reputation?" asked Mahmoud. "He was not only forgiving the son, he was also creating in the son a new heart. He did not have to fear being punished anymore. That brought about reconciliation between the father and the son, who had not been at peace with his father.

It also created a deeper love relationship between the two. "The more I read in the Injil, I discovered that Isa was sent to bring peace between self-centered people and Allah, by sacrificing His life on a cross. When I internalized all this and believed that He died on my behalf, and accepted His forgiveness of my self-centeredness, I experienced a new and wonderful peace. The shame I had carried over not being able to meet Allah's standards was lifted. It was amazing to realize that Allah did not hold anything against me, because the judgment I deserved was paid in full by Isa on my behalf.

"I'll be truthful with you," continued Mahmoud, "I honestly don't fully understand it all, but there is no question about the transformation in my life brought about by coming to know and love Isa. The evidence was peace and joy in my inner being, a new genuine love for people, an assurance of sins forgiven and the enjoyment of an intimate relationship with Allah. I am very aware that I have much more growing to do."

"Mahmoud, where can I get a copy of the Injil?" asked the doctor. "I think I owe it to myself to get better acquainted with this Isa."

A PERSONAL NOTE

Peace be to you, dear reader.

Offering to grant Dr. Husseini the deepest desire of his heart, is not something new.

God made a similar offer to King Sulayman: *"At Gibeon the LORD appeared to Solomon during the night in a dream, and God said, 'Ask for whatever you want me to give you.'"* (1 Kings 3:5)

In the Injil, Yasou made a similar offer to the blind man outside the city of Jericho: *"Jesus stopped and ordered the man to be brought to him. When he came near, Jesus asked him, 'What do you want me to do for you?'"* (Luke 18:40–41)

Perhaps, like Dr. Husseini, a desire has been ignited in your heart and mind to know more about this Isa or Yasou. Consider the following suggested resources to help fulfill that desire. Know that Allah promised people who seek Him in this manner would find Him: *"You will seek me and find me when you seek me with all your heart."* (Jeremiah 29:13)

If you would like to learn more about the life and teachings of Isa, also called the "Prince of Peace," I suggest the following resources:

TAWRAT, ZABUR, AND INJIL (THE HOLY BIBLE)

For an account of the life of Yasou by Luke in Arabic go to www.arabicbible.com/arabic-bible.html, scroll down to New Testament and click on Luke.

For the English version go to www.bible.is/ENGESV/Luke/1/D

FILM

For the English version go to www.youtube.com/watch?v= 0feZQkHbCkM

For other languages, go to https://www.jesusfilm.org/watch.html
    Select Country
    Look Up map and select language

ABOUT THE AUTHOR

THE AUTHOR: He was born in Iran, educated in India, the United States and Lebanon. He has been a life coach to international students, preparing them to return to their countries after living for many years in the United States. He and his wife currently live in the United States.